Phonic Book 1a by

Introduction

Phonic Book 1a is one of a series of five books designed to help teach the Phonic Programme outlined in The National Literacy Strategy.

Phonic Book R is aimed at the Reception class. Phonic Books 1a & 1b cover the work for Year 1. Phonic Books 2a & 2b cover the work for Year 2.

Each book is designed to facilitate word building skills. The photocopiable worksheets are aimed to be an aid for the busy primary classroom teacher, preparing word level work for the Literacy Hour. The photocopiable sheets contain a variety of activities - cloze procedure, muddled words, tracking activities, word crosses and word searches. Much use is made of "Word Building Trains" to encourage children to build their own words. All of these activities aim to reinforce phonic blends until they become automatic to the child.

These books can be used in conjunction with the Read, Write and Spell series of six books which cover the High and Medium Frequency Words outlined in the National Literacy Strategy available directly from Topical Resources.

Topical Resources publishes a range of Educational Materials for use in Primary Schools and Pre-School Nurseries and Playgroups.

For latest catalogue:
Tel: 01772 863158
Fax: 01772 866153

E.Mail:sales@topical-resources.co.uk
Visit our Website on:
www.topical-resources.co.uk

Copyright © 2000 Pat Lamb
Illustrated by Pat Lamb

Printed in Great Britain for "Topical Resources", Publishers of Educational Materials, P.O. Box 329, Broughton, Preston, PR3 5LT by T.Snape & Company Ltd, Boltons Court, Preston.
Cover design and layout by
Paul Sealey Illustration & Design, 3 Wentworth Drive, Thornton

First Published January 2000
ISBN 1 872977 49 9

Contents

Teacher's Notes

This book is designed to facilitate phonic word building skills. The photocopiable worksheets are aimed to be an aid for the busy primary classroom teacher, preparing word level work for the literacy hour. The photocopiable sheets contain a variety of activities - cloze procedure, muddled words, tracking activities, word crosses and word searches. These aim to reinforce phonic blends until they become automatic to the child.

Phonic Word Lists

At the front of books 1a, 1b, 2a and 2b you will find phonic lists of words which can be used as weekly spelling lists. The children should learn no more than fifteen in a week which should be copied into a spelling book, to go home with them. Parents can be encouraged to get the children to practise their spellings by writing them down. Evidence shows that they will be more likely to be retained in the child's visual memory by practising this way rather than orally. Children should be encouraged to write their list down in cursive handwriting. Again, evidence shows this aids memory. Children might also be encouraged to practise spelling lists on the computer. A type size of between 12 and 18 point text should be used.

Children should be encouraged to segment words they are learning to spell ie; break a word or part of a word down into it's component phonemes (eg; c-a-t; ch-ar-t; g-r-ou-n-d).
They should also be encouraged to use the "look, say, cover, write, check" strategy to help commit new words to memory.

Phonic Record

This is an individual record of the phonic blends covered in books R, 1a, 1b, 2a and 2b. Copies of the Phonic Record Sheet can be found near the beginning of Books 1a, 1b, 2a and 2b only.(Book R contains a Letter Recognition Record Sheet.) These can be particularly useful when setting Individual Education Plans for Special Needs children with spelling problems. They can also be used as a spelling/phonic record to follow the child through the school.

Word Building Trains

The word building trains often found at the beginning of the phonic activity sheets are a vital part of developing word building skills. They can be copied onto the board and be the starting point of the phonic lesson. Children can be encouraged to find words and then act them out for others to guess what they are. They could also give the other children in the group verbal clues for them to guess the word.It can also be useful for the children to help decide on the most useful words from those built, to put in their weekly spelling list. They thus feel more involved and are more likely to learn words they have chosen.

It is important to remember that much discussion and word building practice should take place either individually, in a small group or in a whole class situation before a child attempts any of the written exercises.

Homework

Books 1a, 1b, 2a and 2b all contain revision exercises to remind children of how to build words they have encountered in previous lessons. These activities would be suitable for written homework tasks, provided an adult reminds the children of the sounds being used.

Alf and Bet

The cartoon characters Alf and Bet are used to introduce the activities on each page. The same characters are used in the parallel series of books Read, Write and Spell High Frequency Words. Over a period of time the children will become familiar with these two characters and the activities they are asked to do gradually becoming more independent in their work.

Certificates

Alf and Bet Word Sound Reward Certificates can be found on page 6 of Phonic Book 2a. These can be used to encourage children in their progress through their phonic work. A simpler version dealing with individual letters can be found on page 64 of Book R.

High Frequency Words

Topical Resources publishes a parallel series of books to help pupils Read, Write and Spell High Frequency Words. (For more details, ring 01772 863158 and ask for a catalogue.)

Phonic Record Sheet

Name: _____

Phonic Book R

Reception

- ch- (chin)
- sh- (shop)
- th- (thin)
- th- (this)

Phonic Book 1A

Year 1 Term 1 Short vowel sounds (cvc)

- -a- (cat)
- -e- (hen)
- -i- (bin)
- -o- (pot)
- -u- (cut)

Year 1 Term 2 word endings

- -ck (duck)
- -ff (off)
- -ll (doll)
- -ss (miss)
- -ng (sing)

Initial consonant clusters (2 letters)

- bl- (black)
- br- (bring)
- cl- (clap)
- cr- (crab)
- dr- (drop)
- dw- (dwell)
- fl- (flag)
- fr- (frog)
- gl- (glad)
- gr- (grin)
- pl- (plum)
- pr- (pram
- sc- (scab)
- sk- (skip)
- sl- (slip)
- sm- (smack)
- sn- (snip)
- sp- (spot)
- st- (stop)
- sw- (swim)
- tr- (trip)
- tw- (twin)

Initial consonant cluster (3 letters)

- scr- (scrap)
- shr- (shred)
- spl- (splash)
- spr- (spring)
- squ- (squash)
- str- (string)
- thr- (thrush)

Phonic Book 1B

Common end clusters

- -ld (old)
- -nd (land)
- -lk (milk)
- -nk (think)
- sk (flask)
- -lp (help)
- -mp (jump)
- -sp (crisp)
- -ct (fact)
- -ft (lift)
- -lt (belt)
- -nt (bent)
- -pt (slept)
- -st (lost)
- -xt (next)
- -lf (self)
- -nch (bunch)
- -lth (health)

Year 1 Term 3 Long vowel phonemes

- ee (feet)
- ea (sea)
- ai (train)
- a-e (hate)
- ay (play)
- ie (lie)
- i-e (bite)
- igh (night)
- y (fly)
- oa (boat)
- o-e (hole)
- ow (show)
- oo (moon)
- u-e (tune)
- ew (flew)
- ue (blue)

Phonic Book 2A

Year 2 Term 1 Vowel phonemes

- u (full)
- oo (book)
- ar (car)
- oy (toy)
- oi (boil)
- ow (cow)
- ou (shout)

Year 2 Term 2

- air (chair)
- are (care)
- ere (there)
- ear (bear)
- or (horn)
- oor (door)
- aw (draw)
- au (caught)
- ore (store)
- er (herb)
- ir (bird)
- ur (burn)

Year 2 Term 3

- ear (hear)
- ea (head)

Phonic Book 2B

Revision Year 2

Word list

a	e	i	o	u
cat	get	pig	got	but
bag	ten	six	dog	run
can	men	his	nod	dug
ran	red	did	box	sun
man	pen	dig	not	cup
hat	bed	him	pot	rug
had	web	big	fox	sum
dad	pet	sit	top	bus
fat	let	zip	mop	mum
	hen	bin	job	jug

ck	ll	ff	ss	ng
duck	ball	off	pass	bang
sack	tall	huff	less	hang
quack	bell	puff	mess	sang
rock	shell	muff	kiss	king
sock	fill	cuff	miss	thing
pick	hill		hiss	wing
quick	doll		moss	long
shock	bull		toss	song
thick	pull		boss	lung
neck	wall		puss	hung

ch	sh	th (this)	th (thin)	bl
chin	she	this	thin	black
chat	shop	that	thick	bled
chop	ship	then	three	block
chip	shut	them	thing	bless
chum	shed	than	moth	blob
chess	shell	they	path	blot
chill	wish	with	bath	blush
rich	fish			bluff
such	push			block
much	rush			blue

br	cl	cr	dr	fl
brick	clap	cram	dress	flag
bring	clip	crack	drip	flap
brush	class	crash	drop	flip
brim	clock	cross	drill	flat
brass	click	crush	drag	flock
brag	cliff	crab	drum	flash
bran	cling	crib	dram	fling
	club	cress	drab	fluff
	cluck	crop	**dw**	flush
	clang	crag	dwell	flop

fr	gl	gr	pl	sc
from	glass	gran	plan	scab
frog	glad	grab	plug	scum
frock	glen	grass	plush	
fresh	glum	gram	plot	
Fred	glut	grin	plush	
fret		grit	**pr**	**sk**
frill		grim	pram	skim
		grub	prick	skid
		gruff	press	skip
		green	prong	skin
		grill		

sl	sm	sn	sp	st
slab	smack	snap	spin	step
slap	small	snip	spill	stop
slim	smell	sniff	spit	still
slip	smash	snug	spot	stick
slot		snack	spell	sting
slash			span	stack
slush			speck	stuck
slack				stiff
slab				stuff
slick				stung
				stall

sw	tr	tw	spr	scr
swell	trap	twin	spring	scram
swill	trip	twig	sprig	scrap
swim	tram		spat	scrub
swim	track		sprung	
swam	truck			
swig	trot			
swag	trick			
swing	trek			
swish	trim			
	tree			

spl	shr	thr	squ	str
split	shred	thrush	squid	string
splat	shrub	thrash	squib	strap
splash	shrill	throb	squash	strip
		thrill	squall	strut
		three	squad	strum
			squat	struck
				strung

Word Blending Trains

The Word Blending Train is a simple tool used extensively in this series of books to encourage young children to blend letter sounds together to build their own words.

Many of the activity sheets start with a word building train for the pupil to make his/her own words from. These should only be tackled after group or whole class oral work where the new sound/sounds have been introduced, blended and demonstrated on a board or chart. For this purpose, word train blanks are provided on the opposite page. These could be enlarged onto A3 card, laminated and used with a dry wipe whiteboard pen.

An example using CVC words is given below. Children should be able to select a sound from each part of the train and blend these to build different words: e.g. sat; mat; cat; rat; bat; hat. Wherever possible, each part of the train should represent only one sound or phoneme. A smaller blank train is provided below for use on teacher made worksheets.

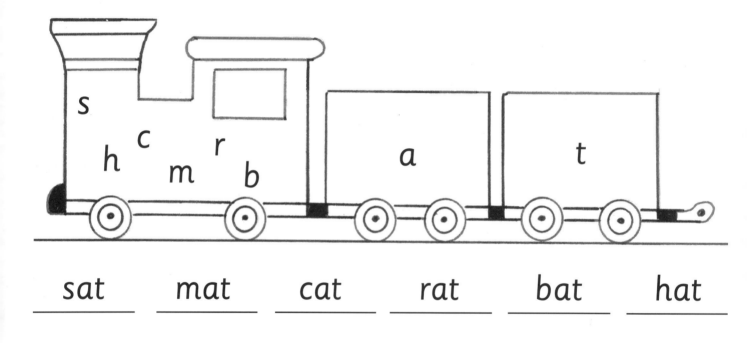

sat	mat	cat	rat	bat	hat

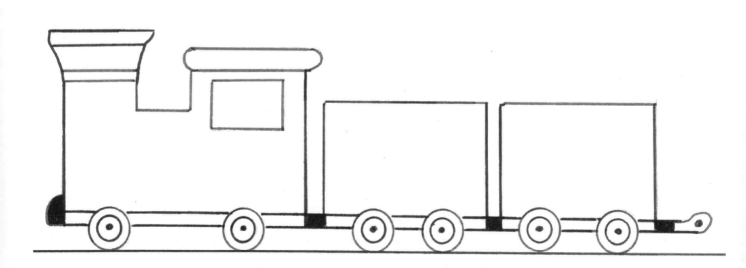

Word Blending Trains

Make an Alphabet Train

(NB. This is not to be confused with the blending train!)

This activity is designed to help pupils revise the alphabet names and sounds.

Each child will need a copy of the trains on the opposite page and the letters to cut out found lower down on this page. (For best results, enlarge the images onto A3 paper).

The children cut out the trains and assemble them in alphabetical order. They can either glue them together using the tabs provided or, glue the whole train onto a strip of coloured paper 8cm x 100cm.

Once assembled, the alphabet train may be used for a variety of activities e.g.

(I)   The children may practice writing the letters on the train sounding them out as they go.
(2)   The children may colour and cut out the lower ease letters and stick them in the correct carriage on the train. Animals or objects may be drawn to illustrate the sound being used.
(3)   The children may colour and cut out the uppercase letters and stick them in the correct carriage on the train.
(4)   The children may colour and cut out the upper <u>and</u> lower case letters and carefully stick them in the correct carriage on the train.
(5)   The finished train can be used to practise saying the letters in alphabetical order.

a	b	c	d	e	f	g	h	i
j	k	l	m	n	o	p	q	r
s	t	u	v	w	x	y	z	
A	B	C	D	E	F	G	H	I
J	K	L	M	N	O	P	Q	R
S	T	U	V	W	X	Y	Z	

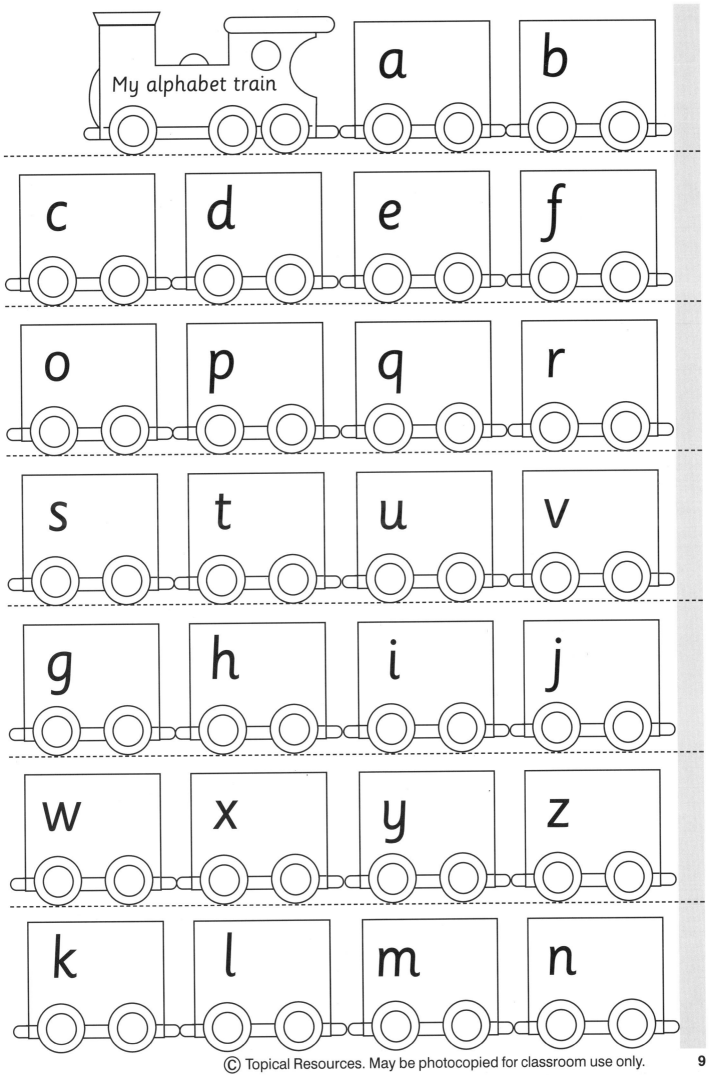

My alphabet train

a b
c d e f
o p q r
s t u v
g h i j
w x y z
k l m n

Name:_____

10

Name: _____

Make the word.

g b a
| b | | |

p t a
| | | |

a h t
| | | |

a t r
| | | |

a n m
| | | |

m j a
| | | |

Sort the words.

Put the 'an' words in the van.

Put the 'at' words in the cat

can

can   mat   man   sat

that   fan   fat   pan   rat   than

Draw a bat on the mat.

Draw a man in a pan.

11

Name:_____

e as in hen

How many words can you make?

d h p K m t | e | n

Add 'e' to the letters.
Put the words in the hen.

j e t   w _ b

g _ t   t _ n

b _ d   l _ g

m _ n

r _ d

jet

Which word? web net bed pet

1. Alf has a _____ snake.

2. Bet is in _____ .

3. The spider is on the _____ .

4. The fish is in the _____ .

Name:_____

Make a word.

t B e

| B | | |

e w b

| | | |

t j e

| | | |

e g l

| | | |

d b e

| | | |

n t e

| | | |

Find the words that rhyme.

hen

pen

ten

red

bed

fed

led

men

then

shed

Draw ten hens in a pen.

Draw Bet in a jet.

13

Name:_____

How many words can you make?

d
n   s
l   p   t
i
p

Add 'i' to the letters.

Put the words in the pig.

b i b

t _ n

w _ n

h _ s

d _ d

bib

h _ m   ch _ n

Which word?   six   dig   thin   zip

1. The hen has _____ eggs. 6

2. Alf likes to _____ .

3. The coat has a _____ .

4. The cat is _____ .

Name:_____

Write the word.

Find the words that rhyme.

Put 'ig' words in this bin.

Put 'in' words in this bin.

'in' words

dig tin
big pin
wig din
fin jig
fig   win

'ig' words

dig

Draw the pictures

A big pig.	A ship.	A zip.

15

Name:_____

How many words can you make?

d
l
b
h
f
j

o

g

Alf

Bet

Add 'o' to the letters.

Put the p**o**t

Alf

g **o** t

f _ x

t _ p

n _ t

n _ d

h _ p

j _ g

d _ g

got

Which word?   dog   dots   pot   box

Bet

1.   Alf is in the _____.

Alf

2.   Bet has a pet _____.

3.   I can see a lot of _____.

4.   The tea- _____ is red and blue.

Name: _____

Find the words that rhyme.

lot

dog
cot
fog
got
hog

hot
cog
not
jog
dot

log

Look for the words. Colour them red.

o	n	f	o	x	t
s	h	o	p	p	o
r	r	o	j	o	b
s	r	o	d	x	o
s	h	c	h	o	p
g	o	t	c	h	o

rod ✓
chop
fox
got
shop
job

Draw a fox, a log and a cot in the box

Name:_____

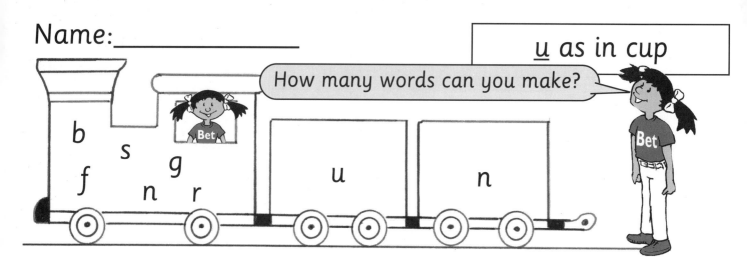

u as in cup

How many words can you make?

b s g f n r

u n

Add 'u' to the letters.

Put the words in the sun.

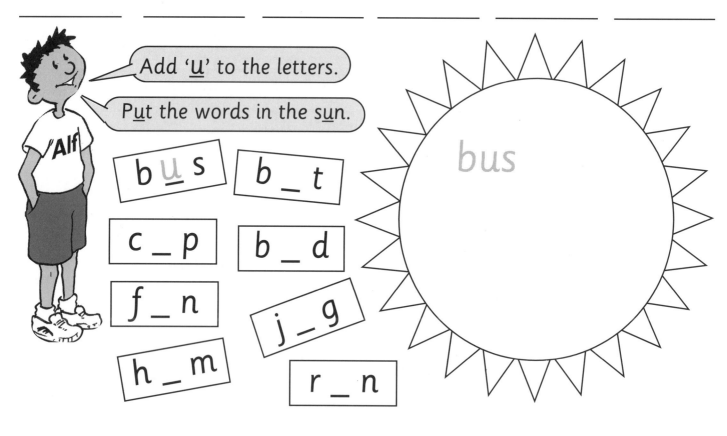

b u s   b _ t

c _ p   b _ d

f _ n   j _ g

h _ m   r _ n

bus

Which word?   hut   rug   mug   sum

1. Can you do this _____ ?   5 + 5 = ☐

2. Bet has a cat on her_____ .

3. The dog sat on the _____ .

4. This is Alf's _____ .

Name:_____

Write the word.

$$\begin{array}{r} 4 \\ + \ 3 \\ \hline \\ \hline \end{array}$$

Find the words. Colour them red.

u	t	f	u	n
u	d	u	g	m
g	s	h	u	t
c	u	b	p	u
d	u	p	u	p
n	u	t	u	t

Tick ✔ the words that rhyme with <u>rug</u>.

cub ✔

nut

fun

shut

dug

pup

mug	
nut	
bug	
tug	
dig	
dug	
hum	
hug	
jug	

Draw the pictures.

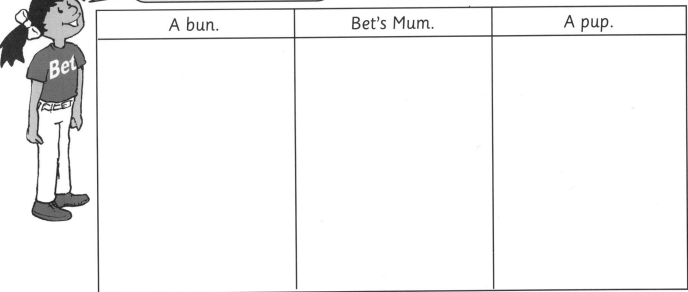

A bun.	Bet's Mum.	A pup.

Name:_____ | Can you remember? | a, e, i, o, u

Choose the right word.

cap	hat	dog	leg	tin
(cup)	hot	dig	log	ten

Put in the missing word.

1. Alf cut his _____ .

2. This is Bet's _____ .

3. I can see _____ flowers.

4. Alf broke   a _____ .

5. Bet has a blue _____ .

Find the rhyming words and colour them the same.

dig — red
cat — blue
did — green
log — yellow
six — pink
big
dog
hid
rat
fix

Can you remember? a, e, i, o, u

Fill in the crossword puzzles.

j

6

10

Name:_____ | Can you remember? | a, e, i, o, u

Alf

Write the words.

web | ____ | ____ | ____ | ____

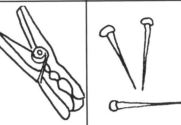 | | $3 + 3 = \square$
 $2 + 1 = \square$
 $4 + \square = 5$ | |

____ | ____ | ____ | ____ | ____

Can you find the words in here?

Bet

p	e	g	l	a	p	i	n	s	a
a	m	j	a	m	e	c	u	p	s
b	o	x	i	x	w	e	b	e	n
u	r	a	t	e	s	u	m	s	o
l	e	g	s	a	o	d	o	t	s

Look for these words. Colour them red.

b	u	t	u	h	i	s
o	p	t	h	e	m	t
s	h	o	p	h	i	g
b	c	h	i	n	r	t
d	a	t	a	r	a	n

ran

chin

but ✓

his

them

shop

Alf

Name:_____

ck as in duck

How many words can you make?

b
s
st
r
p
sh
a
ck

Sort the words.

Put words that rhyme with ki**ck** in this sa**ck**.

kick

Put words that rhyme with so**ck** in this sa**ck**.

sock

sick   rock   lick

shock   pick   lock   dock   quick

thick   mock

Draw the pictures.

Alf is si**ck** in bed.	Bet is on a ro**ck**.

Name:_____

Add 'ck' to the letters.

Put the words in my sock.

Bet

sa c k

ne _ _

si _ _

ki _ _

lo _ _

du _ _

pe _ _

qua _ _

sack

Which word?   duck   kick   neck   tick

Alf

1.   "I can _____ the ball," said Alf.

2.   Can you _____ ✔ my sums please?

3.   The _____ is in the box.

4.   This is Alf's _____.

Alf

Join with a line the words that rhyme.

quack quack

peck

suck

thick

pack

sack

neck

rock

sock

luck

tick

25

Name:_____

How many words can you make?

b
c
f
t
w
h

Bet

all

Find the words. Colour them red.

Bet

Tick ✔ the words that rhyme with **fell**.

d	c	h	i	l	l
b	u	l	l	a	l
d	b	i	l	l	e
m	e	d	o	l	l
a	b	e	l	l	e
b	a	l	l	o	b

bill ✔
bell
ball
bull
doll
chill

bell	
call	
well	
pill	
shell	
tell	
tall	
yell	

Draw Jack and Jill on a hill.

Name:_____

Add 'll' to the letters.

Write the word on the wall.

ta ll

do _ _

ye _ _

bu _ _

fi _ _   ca _ _

te _ _   she _ _

tall

Which word?   fell   doll   tall   full

1. Bet has a rag _____ .

2. Alf _____ and cut his leg.

3. The bag is _____ of apples.

4. Bet is not as _____ as Alf.

Colour red the words that rhyme with pill.

bull   bill   bell   fill   fall   till   tell   will   mill   chill   well

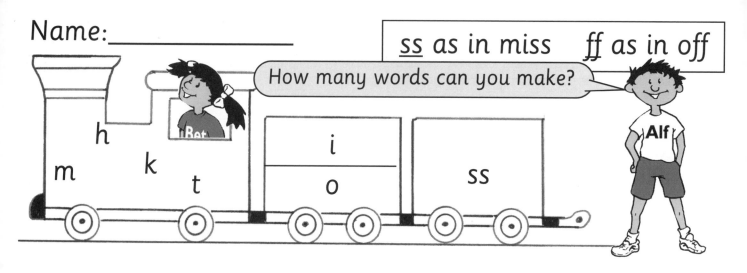

Name:_____

ss as in miss   ff as in off

How many words can you make?

m h k t   i / o   ss

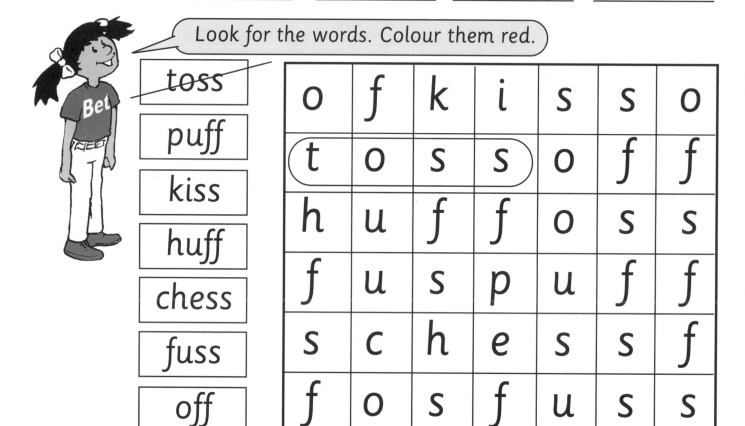

Look for the words. Colour them red.

| toss | puff | kiss | huff | chess | fuss | off |

o	f	k	i	s	s	o
t	o	s	s	o	f	f
h	u	f	f	o	s	s
f	u	s	p	u	f	f
s	c	h	e	s	s	f
f	o	s	f	u	s	s

Look for the words that rhyme. Colour them the same.

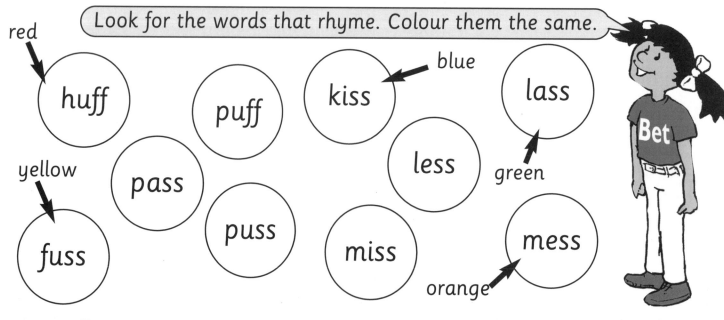

red → huff   puff   kiss ← blue   lass
                                          less   green →
yellow → fuss   pass   puss   miss   mess ← orange

Name:_____

Add 'ss' to the letters. Put the words in Sid Snake.

pa s s   me _ _   fu _ _   ki _ _

to _ _   hi _ _   mi _ _   bo _ _

Sid is cross.

hiss
hi _ _ _
hi _ _ _

pass

Add 'ff' to the letters.

Put the words in Biff the dog.

pu _ _   o _ _ _

hu _ _

Biff

cu _ _

Put in the missing word.
Draw the picture

Draw Puss-in-Boots

Humpty-Dumpty
fell __ __ __ the wall.

29

Name:_____

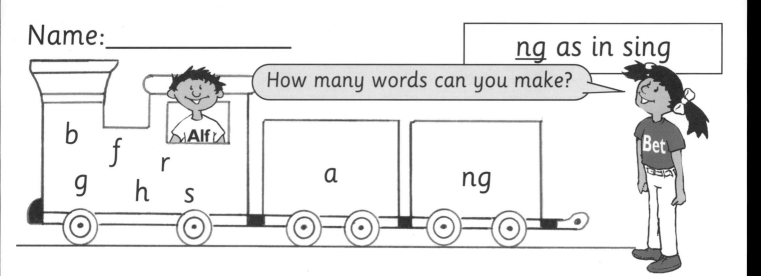

ng as in sing

How many words can you make?

b f r g h s

a

ng

Tick ✔ the words that rhyme with <u>ring</u>.

ding	✔
sing	
hang	
wing	
thing	
lung	
king	

Draw 3 things that you like on the lo<u>ng</u> line.

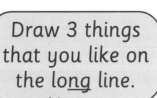

Find the words. Colour them blue.

| ~~bang~~ | rung | song |
| king | hung | long |

k	l	o	n	g	a
b	a	n	g	o	n
i	s	o	n	g	a
n	g	r	u	n	g
h	u	n	g	n	g
n	g	k	i	n	g

Name:_____

Add '**ng**' to the letters.

Put the words on the rungs of the ladder.

Alf

long

lo **ng**

ba _ _

ra _ _

wi _ _

thi _ _

lu _ _

ki _ _

so _ _

Which word? | ring | long | song | king |

Alf

1.   Sid is a _____ snake.

2.   Bet sang a _____ .

Jack and Jill went up the hill ♫

3.   The _____ has got a crown.

4.   Alf likes to _____ the bell.

ding - dong

Colour red the words that rhyme with 'hu**ng**'.
Colour blue the words that rhyme with 'go**ng**'.

rung   long   sung   song   lung   dong

31

Name:_____

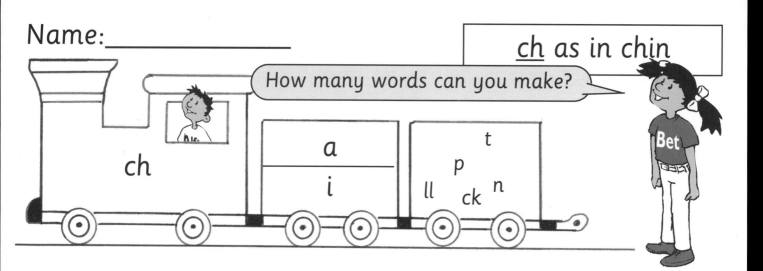

How many words can you make?

ch

a
i

t
p
ll   ck   n

Ring the 'ch' words.

Colour the 'ch' words in Sid.

c	m	u	c	h	c
h	c	h	e	s	s
c	c	h	a	t	h
s	u	c	h	c	u
c	h	r	i	c	h
c	h	i	l	l	t

chat ✓
such
rich
chill
chess
much

chip
rich
ship
much
shop

Draw 3 of your chums. Write their names.

Name:_____

Join the dots and colour.

Write the letters.

ch   ch   _ _

ch
___   ___   ___

Add '**ch**' to the letters.
Write the new words in
the **ch**ick.

ri c h   _ _ in

_ _ um   _ _ at

mu _ _

_ _ eck

su _ _

_ _ op

rich

Which word? chips chin chum chicks

1. Alf cut his _____ .

2. I had fish and _____ today.

3. Fred is Alf's _____ .

4. The hen has two _____ .

33

Name:_____

How many words can you make?

b
r
d
c
m
s

Bet

a

sh

Alf

___sh

Sort the words.

Bet

push
bush
shall
rush
shed
she

posh
shop
shack
wish

sh___

Draw the pictures.

a shell.

a fish on a dish.

Alf

a shop.

a ship

Name:_____

Add 'sh' to the letters.

Write the words in the shed.

s h e

_ _ ut

_ _ op

_ _ ell

wi _ _

fi _ _

ru _ _

_ _ ip

she

Which word? fish   she   bush   shut

1. Bet fell and _____ began to cry.

2. Alf hid in a _____ .

Alf

3. Mum _____ the door.

4. Alf has a pet _____ .

Look for the words. Colour them.

u	s	p	u	s	h
h	u	s	h	s	h
h	b	u	s	h	k
s	h	g	u	s	h
r	u	s	h	o	g

bush - (red)

rush - (blue)

push - (yellow)

hush - (green)

gush - (orange)

Alf

35

Name:_____

th as in this

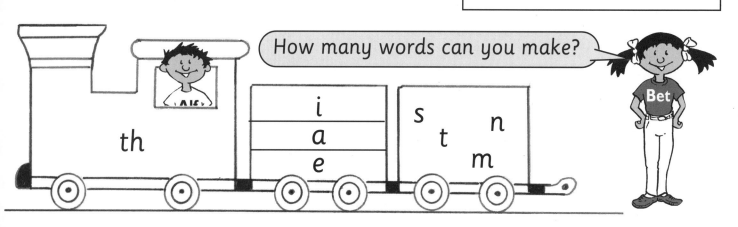

How many words can you make?

th | i a e | s t n m

Join the dots and colour.

Write the letters.

th   th   __

th ___ ___ ___

Which word? | with | This

_____ is my pet.

Can I go _____ Bet, please?

Colour the 'th' words in Sid

Name:_____

Add 'th' to the letters.

t h in   ba _ _   _ _ ick

mo _ _   _ _ ing

_ _ ree   pa _ _

thin

Put the words in the path.

Which word?   thick   thin

This pencil is _ _ _ _ _.

This pencil is _ _ _ _ _ _.

Draw three mo<u>th</u>s.

Draw a ba<u>th</u>.

Colour the 'th' words in Sid.

three   thick   chick   bath   thing   path

37

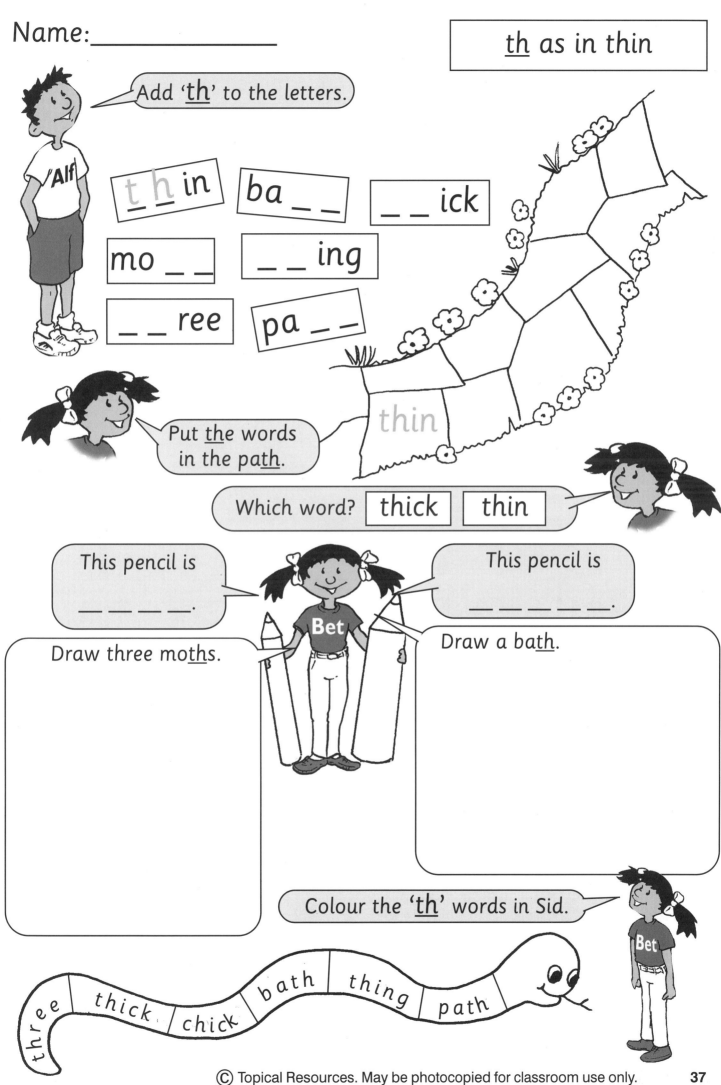

Name:_____

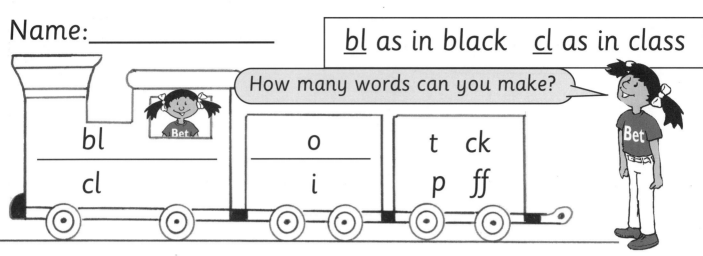

bl as in black   cl as in class

How many words can you make?

bl
cl

o
i

t   ck
p   ff

Which word?   blue   class   bled   clock

1. Bet has a _____ hat.

2. Alf cut his leg and it _____ .

3. I go to bed at 7 o' _____ .

4. Alf and Bet are in _____ 2.

Class 2
Miss Cliff

Draw Bet's blue hat.

Draw your class.

Name:_____

bl

black

Join the dots and colour.

Sort the words. Put them in the correct boxes.

cl

cling

blue

bled

clang

cling

bless

cliff

blob

black

class

clap

Which word?   clock   clang

Bang rhymes with
_ _ _ _ _

Block rhymes with
_ _ _ _ _

Draw and colour a
blue clock.

Alf

Draw and colour a
black blob.

39

Name:_____

fl as in flag   gl in a glass

How many words can you make?

fl
gl

a

n
t
sh
d
p
ss

Which word? flip-flops glass flock flats

1.   Here are Bet's _____ - _____ .

2.   Gran lives in a block of _____ .

3.   Do not drop the _____ Alf.

4.   I can see a _____ of sheep.

Draw the pictures.

Alf is glad.	Alf is glum.

40

Name:_____

fl as in flag gl in a glass

Write what you see.

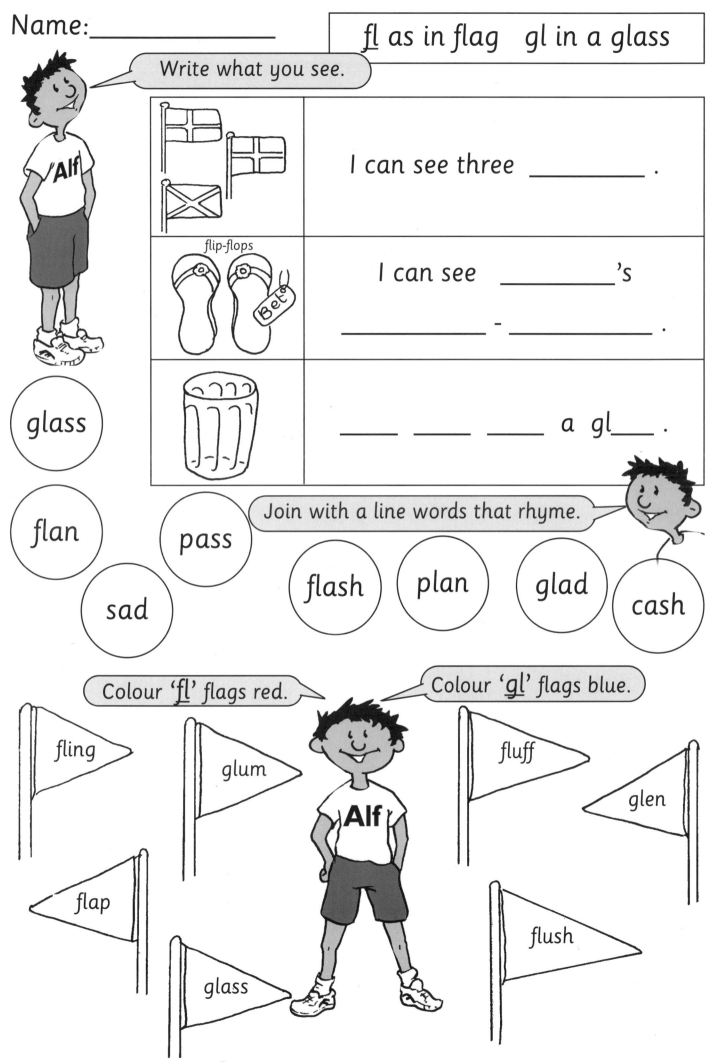	I can see three _____ .
flip-flops	I can see _____'s _____ - _____ .
	___ ___ ___ a gl___ .

glass

flan   pass

sad

Join with a line words that rhyme.

flash   plan   glad   cash

Colour 'fl' flags red.   Colour 'gl' flags blue.

fling   glum   fluff   glen

flap   glass   flush

41

Name:_____

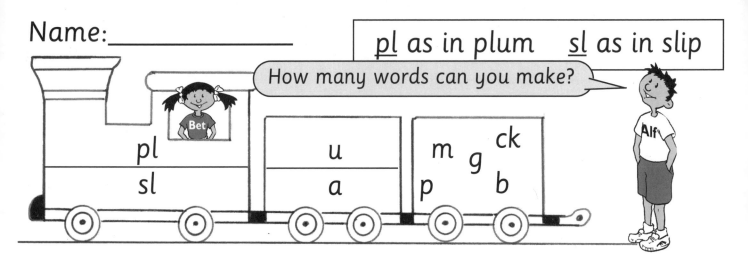

pl as in plum   sl as in slip

How many words can you make?

pl
sl

u
a

m   g   ck
p   b

Ring the correct word?

1.   There are lots of plums / plots on the tree.

2.   "Do not slam / slim the door!" said Mum.

3.   "My trousers are too slick / slack," said Alf.

4.   The kettle has a plug / slug on it.

Colour the slugs with '__sl__' words in.

slit

plan

slip

Bet

sling

slush

slam

plush

Name:_____

pl or sl ?

| _ _ a b | _ _ _ u g | _ _ i m | _ _ i p |

| _ _ a n | _ _ a c k | _ _ u m | _ _ a m |

Find the rhyming words. Colour them the same.

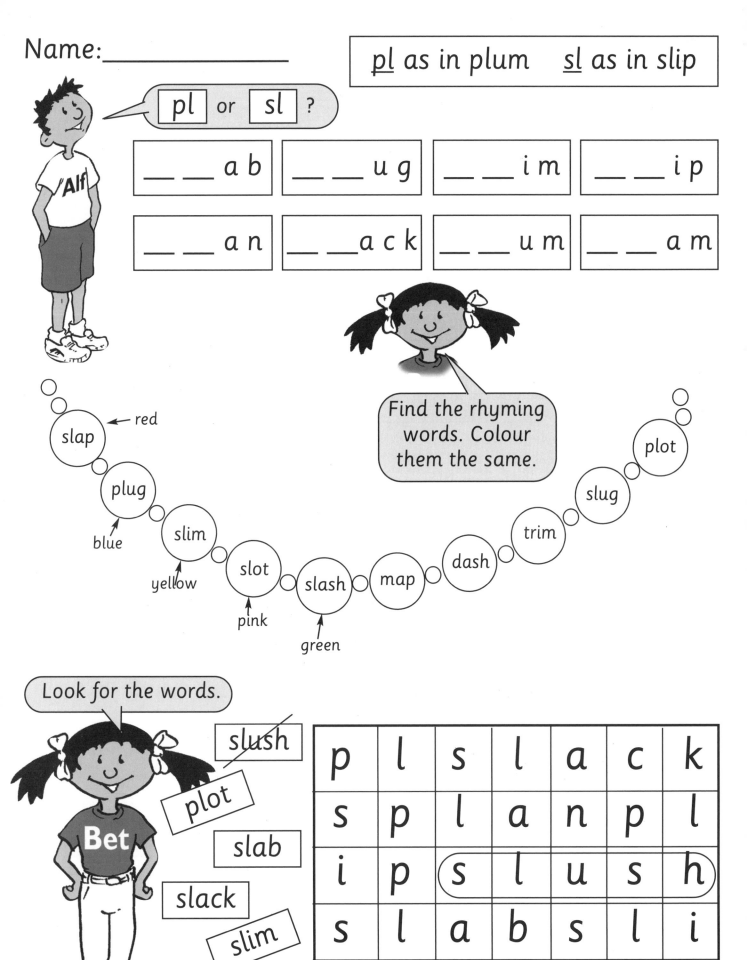

slap ← red
plug — blue
slim — yellow
slot — pink
slash — green
map
dash
trim
slug
plot

Look for the words.

slush
plot
slab
slack
slim
plan

p	l	s	l	a	c	k
s	p	l	a	n	p	l
i	p	s	l	u	s	h
s	l	a	b	s	l	i
p	l	s	l	i	m	s
p	l	o	t	s	l	i

43

Name:_____

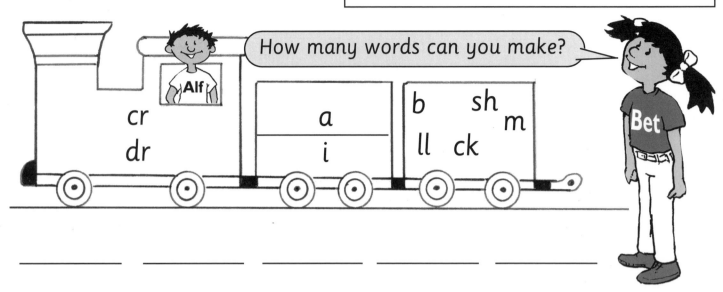

How many words can you make?

cr
dr

a
i

b   sh
         m
ll   ck

____ ____ ____ ____

Which word? dress crack drum crab

1. The cup has a __ __ __ __ __ __ in it.

2. Bet has a blue __ __ __ __ __ .

3. Alf likes to bang his __ __ __ __ .

4. Alf has a __ __ __ __ in his net.

Colour the 'dr' words red.
Colour the 'cr' words blue.

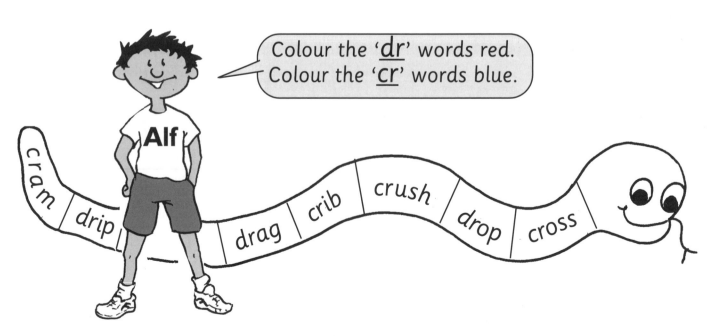

cram   drip   drag   crib   crush   drop   cross

Name:_____

Join the dots and colour..

Bet

Can you do the word sums?

cr + ack = crack _____

dr + ag = _____

cr + oss = _____

cr + ush = _____

dr + ill = _____

dr + ess = _____

Ring the correct word.

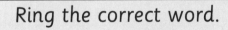

1. Dad had a crash / ~~crush~~ in his van.

2. The tap began to drip / drop .

3. Did you crop / drop the cup, Bet?

4. Alf is cross / dress .

45

Name:_____

How many words can you make?

br
pr

i
a

ck
ng
m

_____ _____ _____ _____

Which word? | Grass | bring | pram | grub |

I put my doll in the
_ _ _ _ _ .

Can you _ _ _ _ _ _
me my hat please, Alf?

I can see a
_ _ _ _ _
in this apple.

_ _ _ _ _ _ is green.

Draw the pictures.

Gran with a <u>gr</u>in.	Bet in a <u>pr</u>am.	A <u>br</u>ick wall.

Name:_____

br as in bring gr as in grin pr as in pram

How many words can you make?

gr

i
a

p   ll   t
b   n

Sort the words.

br   pr   gr

brass   prop   gruff   brag   grip
pram   brim   grab   press

Colour green the grubs with 'gr' words in.

grit   prick

How many green grubs?

prong   gran   bring

brick   grass   press

gram

Name:_____

fr as in frog   **tr** as in trip

How many words can you make?

tr
fr

i
o

p   ck
m   g

Which word? | frog | from | Fred |

Alf's chum is
_ _ _ _ _ .

Fred has a pet
_ _ _ _ .

Draw Fred.

This is Fred's _ _ _ _ _ .

Alf has a frog too.
He got it _ _ _ _ _ Fred.

Draw Alf with his frog.

Colour the 'tr' words.

trick | tick | trim | fresh | trot | trill | this

48   © Topical Resources. May be photocopied for classroom use only.

Name:_____

fr as in frog   tr as in trip

Make the words.

ckofr	utrck	gofr	eetr

tr or fr ?

___ o m   ___ i c k   ___ o t   ___ o g

___ a m   ___ e s h   ___ i l l   ___ a c k

Ring the word.
Draw the pictures.

1. Mum has a red and

   blue frog
         frock .

2. Alf and Bet go on

   the school trip
               trap .

Name:_____

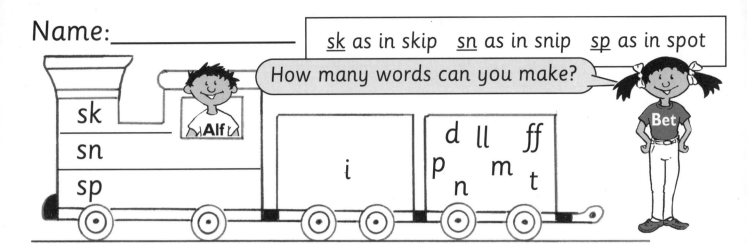

How many words can you make?

sk
sn
sp

Alf   i   d   ll   ff   p   n   m   t   Bet

Ring the words.

1. Can you   spill / spell   'fish'?

   f _ _ h

2. The dog began to   sniff / snip   the bone.

3. Alf is   spin / snug   in bed.

4. Bet can   skid / skip   well.

Colour the 'sp' spots red.
Colour the 'sn' spots yellow.
Colour the 'sk' spots blue.

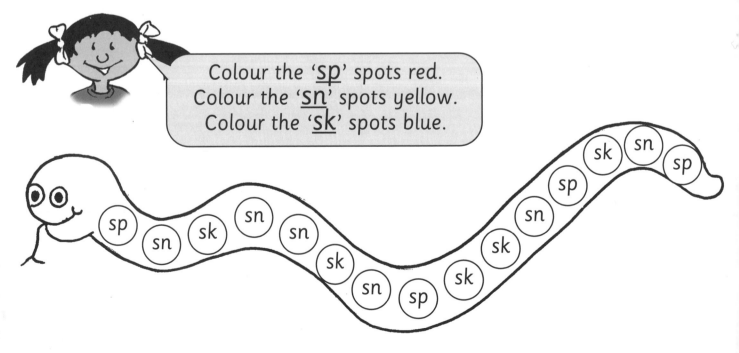

Name:_____

sp or sn ?

_ _ i l l   _ _ i f f   _ _ i p   _ _ a n

sk or sp ?

_ _ e c k   _ _ i m   _ _ i d   _ _ o t s

Which words rhyme? Colour them blue.

spill	fill	sniff	will
snap	trap	snug	snip
skin	skid	skim	spin
speck	neck	snack	skid

Put in the missing words.

Alf has lots of _____ on his face.

Draw the pictures.

Bet can skip.	A snack.	A dog with spots.

51

Name:_____

How many words can you make?

Look for the words.

scab ✓
smell
smash
stiff
steps
scum

t	s	m	e	l	l	a
s	m	a	s	c	u	m
s	m	a	s	h	i	t
s	t	s	t	e	p	s
s	c	a	b	s	t	e
s	m	s	t	i	f	f

st

sc

sm

st

sc

st

sm

sc

Follow the foot-steps
Colour the 'SC' foot-steps red.
Colour the 'sm' foot-steps yellow.
Colour the 'st' foot-steps blue.

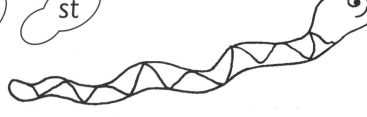

st

sm

sc

st

Name:_____

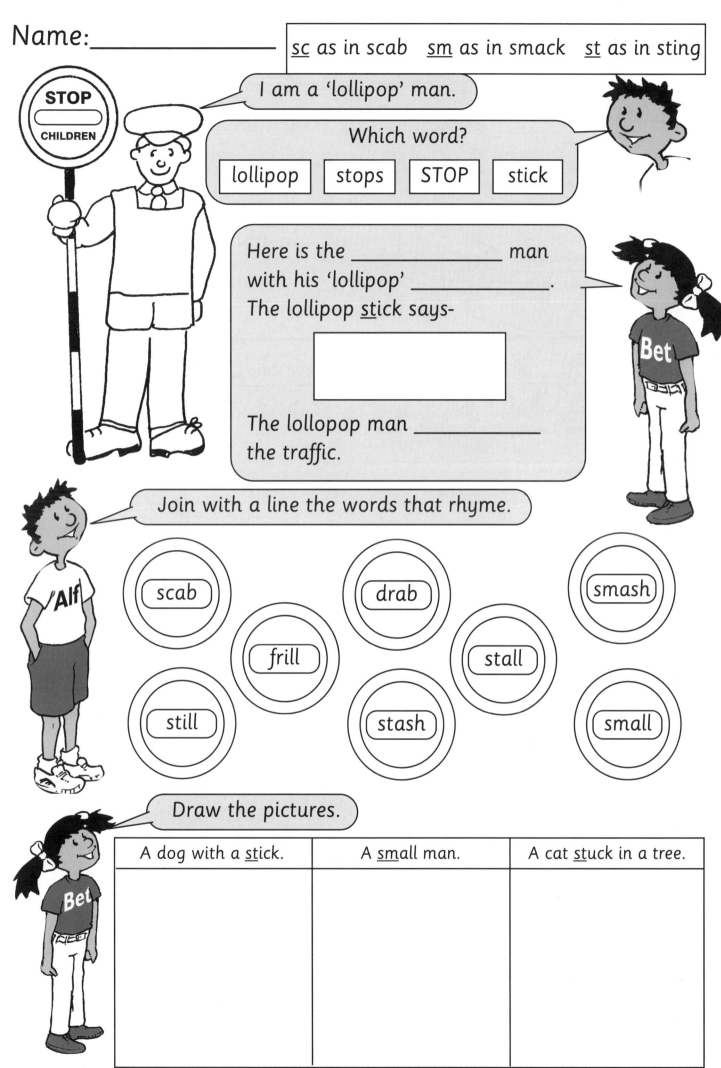

I am a 'lollipop' man.

Which word?

| lollipop | stops | STOP | stick |

Here is the _____ man
with his 'lollipop' _____.
The lollipop stick says-

The lollopop man _____
the traffic.

Join with a line the words that rhyme.

scab

drab

smash

frill

stall

still

stash

small

Draw the pictures.

A dog with a stick.	A small man.	A cat stuck in a tree.

53

Name:_____

Cut out the words. Stick them in the correct boxes to finish the rhymes.

Ding-dong [ ]

Pussy's by the [ ]

Put a pussy by the well.

Jack and [ ]

Went up the [ ]

Draw Jill.

Put Humpty on the wall.

Humpty Dumpty sat

on a [ ] ,

Humpty Dumpty had

a great [ ] .

wall | well | bell | Jill | hill | fall

Name:_____

Write the word.

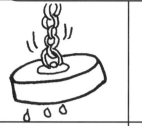   

Can you find the words in here?

c	d	o	l	l	b	e	l	d	a
f	i	s	h	i	p	l	u	g	e
c	l	o	c	k	e	d	u	c	k
p	b	a	l	l	a	c	l	o	c
r	i	n	g	y	b	e	l	l	z

Can you find these words?

g	l	a	d	s	p	l	o	t
b	a	c	h	i	c	k	g	l
a	b	a	t	h	s	l	i	m
s	l	i	p	o	c	l	u	b
r	e	d	i	n	b	l	e	d

bled ✓
club
chick
glad
plot
slip
bath

55

Name:_____ | Can you remember? | **Activity sheet**

Find 2 balls which are coloured the same.

Colour words that rhyme with ball - red.
Colour words that rhyme with ring - blue.
Colour words that rhyme with sack - green.

Colour '<u>st</u>' words - yellow.
Colour '<u>gr</u>' words - pink.

1 sing quack bring pack	2 green shack crack grass	3 grab hall fall gruff
4 small king thing tall	5 step wall stuck call	6 still duck luck stick
7 ball smack fall back	8 stop fling stiff wing	9 grim black track grip

Number [ ] and number [ ] are the same.

Name:_____

Fill in the crosswords. Look across → and down ↓

Gran

Name:_____

sw as in swing   tw as in twin

How many words can you make?

sw
tw

i

m   ng
sh   ll
n   g

_____ _____ __ _____ _____ _____

Which word? swim   twig   swing   twins

1. Alf and Bet are __ __ __ __ __.

2. "I can __ __ __ __ well," said Alf.

3. Bet fell off her __ __ __ __ __ .

4. The bird 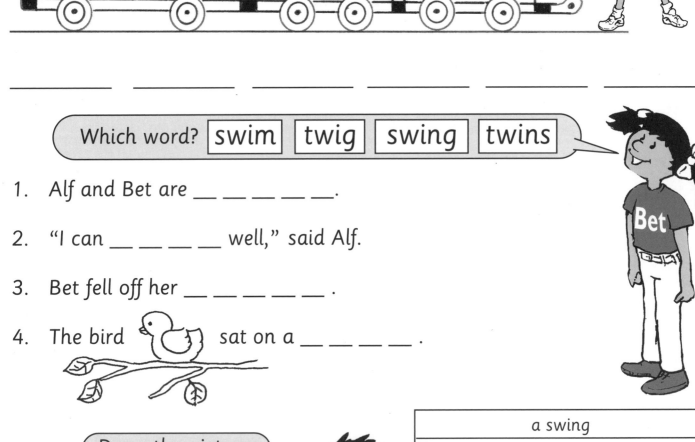 sat on a __ __ __ __ .

Draw the pictures.

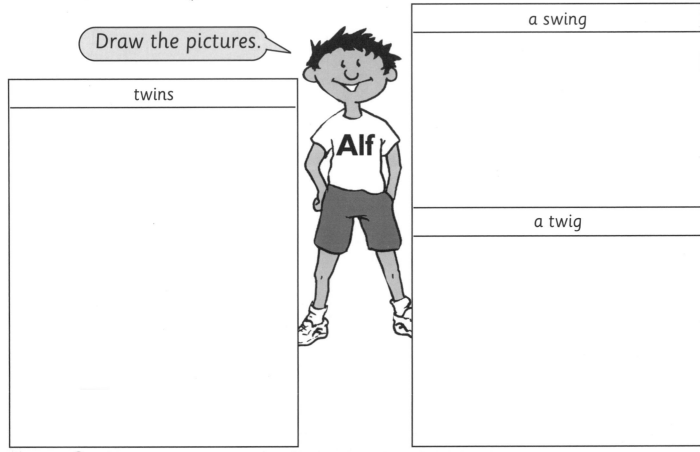

twins

a swing

a twig

Name:_____

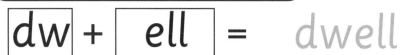

Can you do the word sums?

dw	+	ell	=	dwell
sw	+	im	=	_____
tw	+	ig	=	_____
sw	+	ell	=	_____
tw	+	in	=	_____
sw	+	ing	=	_____

We are t _ _ _ _ _ .

Which words rhyme? Colour them the same.

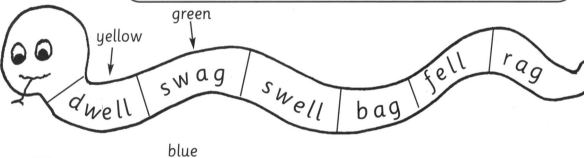

yellow   green

dwell swag swell bag fell rag

blue

red

swing twig swig bring big ring

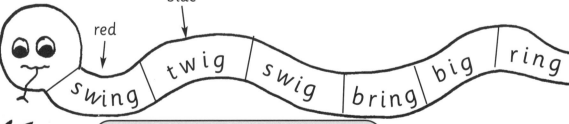

Join the dots and colour.

dw sw tw

59

Name:_____

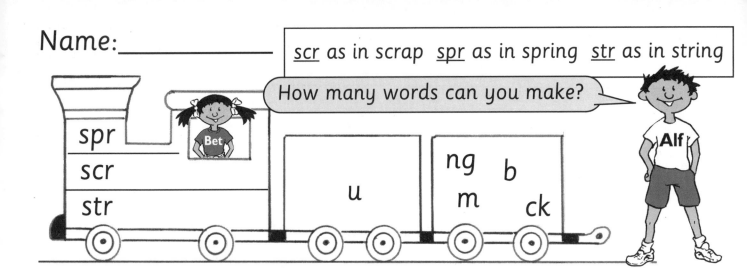

scr as in scrap   spr as in spring   str as in string

How many words can you make?

spr
scr
str

Bet

u

ng
m
b
ck

Alf

Ring the word and draw the pictures.

1.   This cat has a
     ball of   string
               strung   .

2.   This cat has a
     scrap   of fish .
     scrub

Look for the words.

i	s	s	p	r	i	n	g
s	p	r	s	p	r	i	g
s	c	s	p	r	a	t	p
r	s	t	r	i	p	s	c
s	c	r	a	m	s	p	r
a	s	t	r	u	c	k	t

sprat

scram

struck

strip

spring

sprig

Name:_____ | scr as in scrap spr as in spring str as in string

Join the dots on the letters and colour.
Cut out and match to the letters above.
Cut out the words and stick in the correct box.

scr	spr	str

str   scr   spr

scrub	sprig	strip	sprat	string
scrap	strum	spring	scram	

61

Name:_____

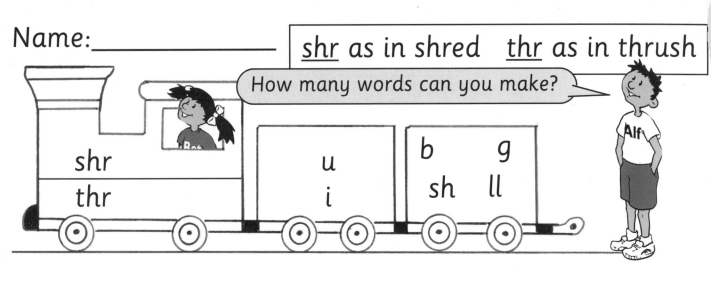

How many words can you make?

shr
thr

u
i

b   g
sh   ll

Which word?

shrub   thrush

A _ _ _ _ _ _ _
is a bird.

A _ _ _ _ _ _
is a bush.

Draw a dog with three pups.

Colour 'shr' in this snake.

Colour 'thr' in this snake.

© Topical Resources. May be photocopied for classroom use only.

Name:_____

How many words can you make?

spl   a / i   sh   t

_____   _____   _____

Which word? Squash splash splits.

1. Alf likes to _____ in puddles.

2. Dad _____ the logs with an axe.

3. "Do not _____ my flowers," said Mum.

Colour 'spr' in this snake.

spr | rsp | spr | psr | spr | rps   spr | srp | squ | spr

Colour 'squ' in this snake.

spr | squ | squ | suq | squ | spr   squ | uqs

63

Name:_____

shr as in shred spl as in splash
squ as in squash thr as in thrush

Put the words in the correct house.

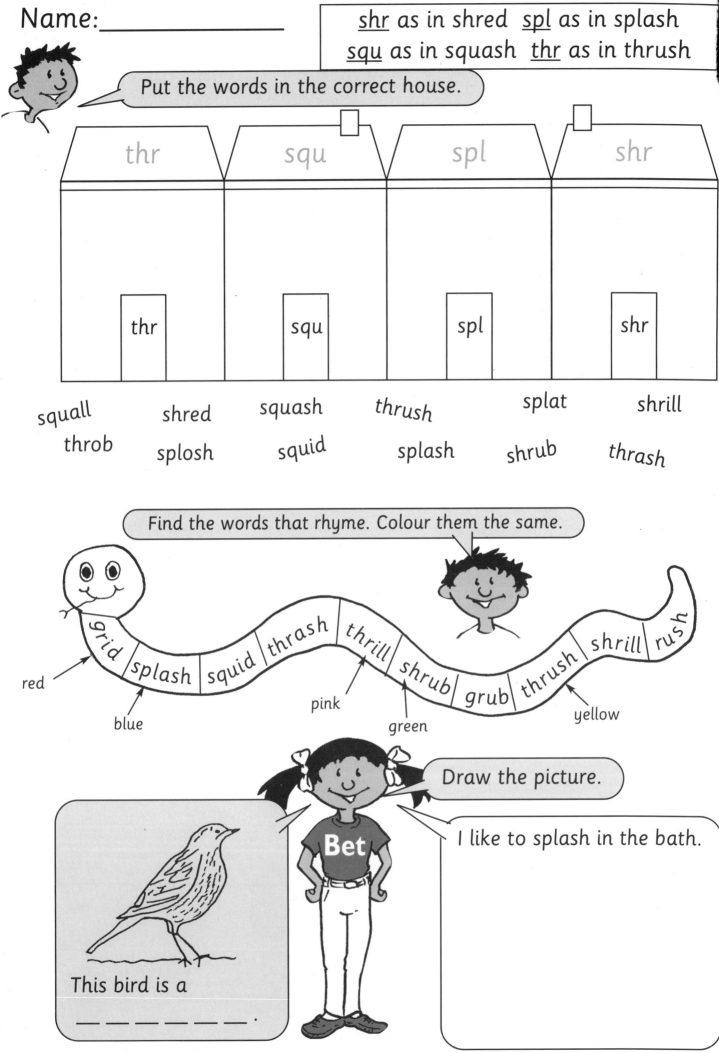

thr   squ   spl   shr

thr   squ   spl   shr

squall   shred   squash   thrush   splat   shrill
throb   splosh   squid   splash   shrub   thrash

Find the words that rhyme. Colour them the same.

grid splash squid thrash thrill shrub grub thrush shrill rush

red
blue
pink
green
yellow

Draw the picture.

Bet

I like to splash in the bath.

This bird is a

_ _ _ _ _ _ .

© Topical Resources. May be photocopied for classroom use only.